On a Camel to the Moon

and other poems about journeys

Compiled by Valerie Bloom
Illustrated by Garry Parsons

Belitha Press

Contents

On a Camel to the Moon

and other poems about journeys

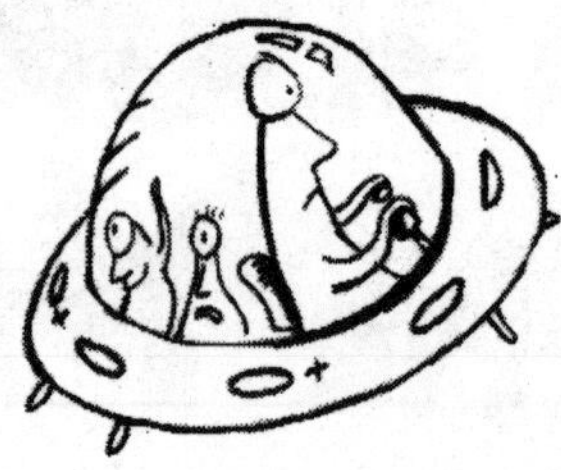

First published in Great Britain in 2001 by

Belitha Press Limited,
London House, Great Eastern Wharf
Parkgate Road, London SW11 4NQ

Series editors: Pie Corbett, Mary-Jane Wilkins
Editors: Russell Mclean, Stephanie Turnbull
Designer: Sarah Goodwin

ISBN 1 84138 247 7 (hardback)
ISBN 1 84138 257 4 (paperback)

British Library Cataloguing in Publication Data
for this book is available from the British Library.

Printed by Omnia Books Ltd, Glasgow

10 9 8 7 6 5 4 3 2 1

Journey

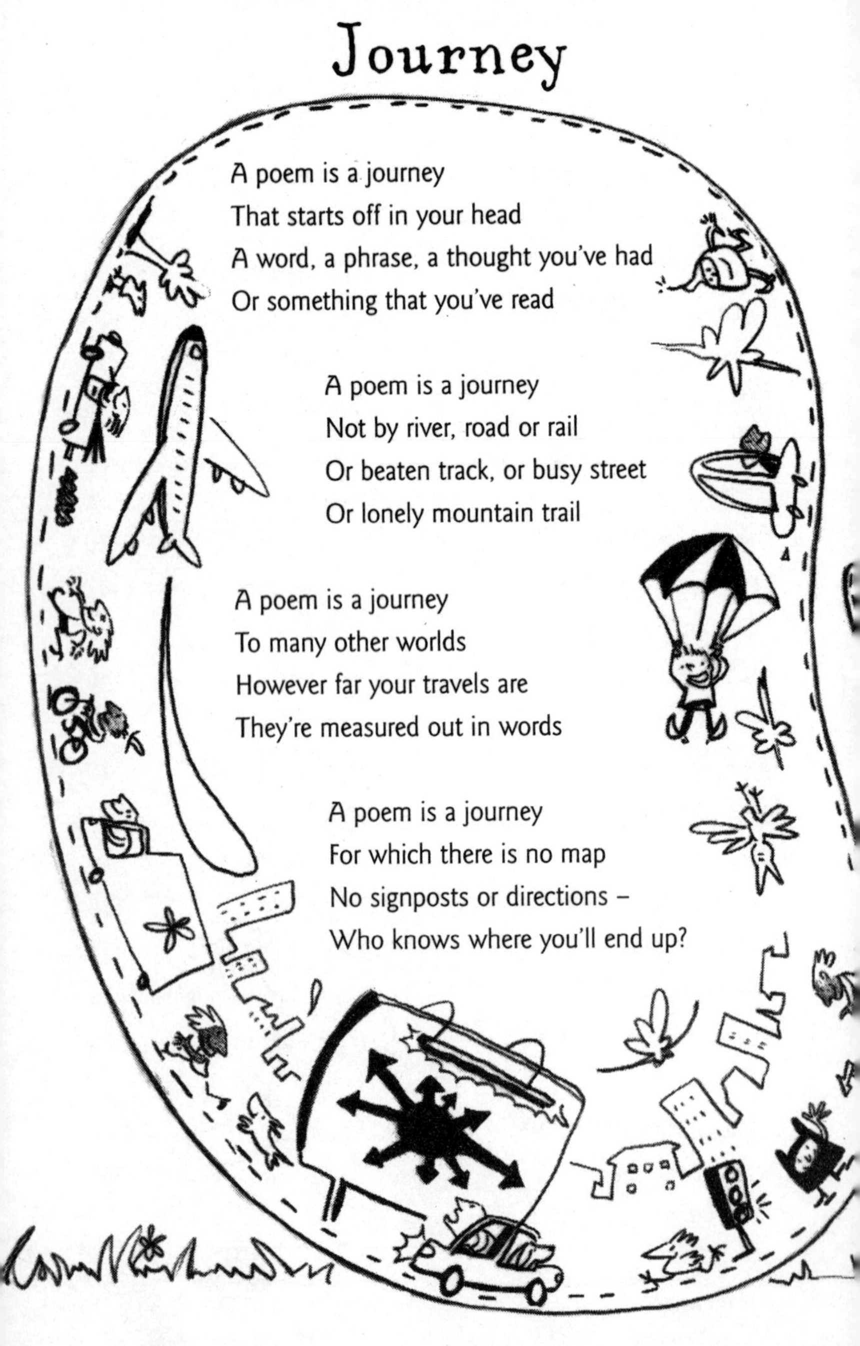

A poem is a journey
That starts off in your head
A word, a phrase, a thought you've had
Or something that you've read

A poem is a journey
Not by river, road or rail
Or beaten track, or busy street
Or lonely mountain trail

A poem is a journey
To many other worlds
However far your travels are
They're measured out in words

A poem is a journey
For which there is no map
No signposts or directions –
Who knows where you'll end up?

A poem is a journey
To lose and find yourself
To go somewhere, to stay right here
To be somebody else

A poem is a journey
To places far and strange
There's only one thing that's for sure –
You won't come back the same.

James Carter

The Blue Yonder

There are days when the world zings.
Dad sniffs the air,
puts down his paper and says 'Today!
I can smell a holiday!'
And we'd be off
stuffing the boot of the car with buckets and spades,
swimming cozzies, sunscreen, raincoats, jam,
whole drawers full of clothes,
towels, the ball, comics,
a sliced loaf, the dog.

Off we'd go
'Into the wild blue yonder'
mapless and free.
In the back we dozed and hummed,
elbows poked, someone pinched.
We played Spot and Snap and I Spy.
We wrestled and we sang 'Are we nearly there yet?
Are we nearly there?'

Always just that bit further on,
over the hill and faraway,
round the corner, round the bend,
the golden place, rainbow's end.
Meanwhile, sticky and sickening we fidget and fret
keep the window rolled right down ready for any stray sunbeam.
We strain our ears, we hope, we peer. Are we nearly there yet?
Are we near?

Michaela Morgan

Sea Dream

I wander the deep-sea forests
where the snake-fish slither;
where the dark dunes drift
like rolling mist
and the white whales murmur.

I wake to coral blossom
and sleep in a star-clad cave;
my bed is a glade
of ribboned jade,
my sky a wave.

I dance by the spiny urchin
and ride the giant clam;
I feel as I sail
the dolphin's tail
the sad whale song.

Judith Nicholls

The Osprey

Suddenly from the sea
a migrating angel on its way
from Lapland to Africa
took a break at Cwmtydu.
It stayed three weeks,
like the moon roosting in an oak.

They fed it like a pet
on slithering buckets of silver
left over from the fish shop.
You could tell it was happy
by the way it splintered the sun
with its snowbird wings.

But its mind was on Africa,
the glittering oceans, the latitudes
sliding beneath its heart.
'Stay!' they said. 'Stay!'
But one day it lifted off and turned south
for the red desert, for the red sun.

Gillian Clarke

Dragon on the Bus

Now, you know I'm not a wuss.
I don't like to make a fuss,
but there's just a little matter that I think we should discuss...
There's a dragon on the bus!
There's a dragon on the bus!
There's a dragon on the bus and it's looking at us!

Let me speak to an inspector
or a company director
'cos I don't quite recollect a
sign to say we should expect a
scaly people-vivisector on this bus.

Now, I never swear and cuss,
but it's flipping obvious
that we've got a situation here that could be hazardous.
There's a dragon on the bus!
There's a dragon on the bus!
There's a dragon on the bus and it's com[illegible] us!

I think we should call a meeting
'cos its fiery breath is heating
all our clothing and our seating.
I don't like the way it's treating
all the people that it's eating on this bus.

It's chewing us and burning us
and this is what's concerning us.
It could become a problem by the time we reach the terminus.
There's a dragon on the bus!
There's a dragon on the bus!
There's a dragon on the bus and it's eating
and it's eating
and it's eating all of us!

Nick Toczek

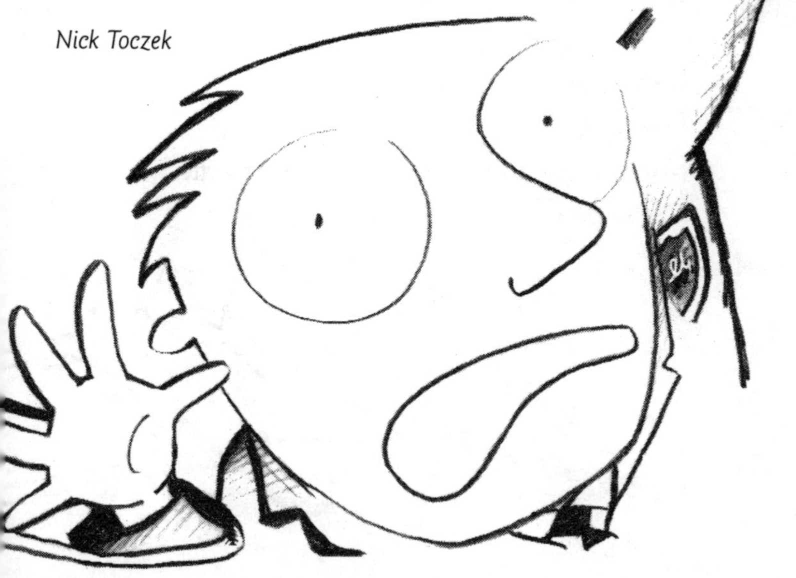

In an Airplane

The ground recoils beneath us as we speed away from Earth,
There's a roar like a volcano or a hippo giving birth,
Our silver stallion leaps the clouds, thunders towards the blue,
And we gasp in wonder at the sight that opens to our view.

The golden ball is slowly sinking, but before it goes
It sheds its light on blue and white and fashions bright rainbows
From drops of moisture – tears of mist and sweat of hurrying cloud,
Wispy trees stand to attention, ethereal and proud.

The cotton-candy mountains rise like titans on the right,
Below, the azure rivers lap the beaches of the night,
Wide fields of fleecy crops stretch for miles like virgin snow,
And softly shifting fingers point the way that we should go.

Valerie Bloom

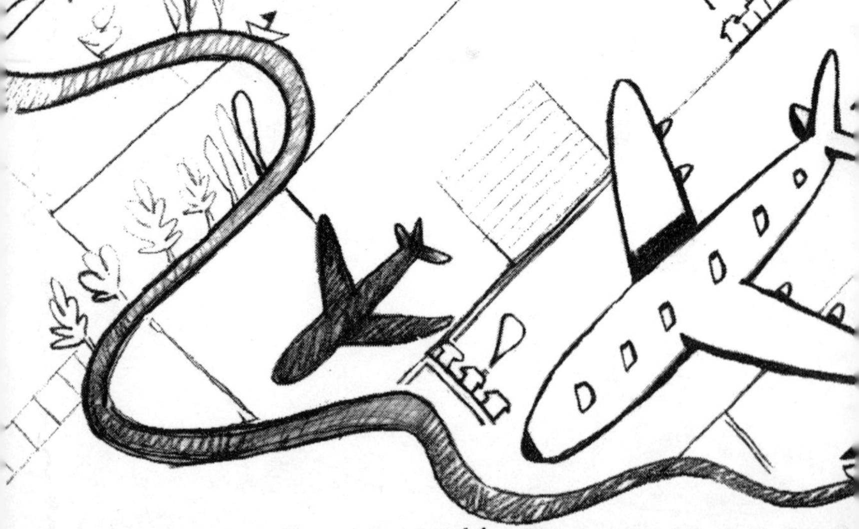

Night Ride

Sky-black
Tarmac,
Each car
A shooting star!

Sue Cowling

The Traveller

It has taken three days to travel this far
My burden is heavy, my foot is sore
I move on by night in the glow of the moon
With luck on my side I'll be there soon.

My stalky eyes have seen many sights
And I value the company I've shared on these nights.
I've conversed with a beetle, parleyed with a mouse,
Whom I met as I trailed past the wall of the house.

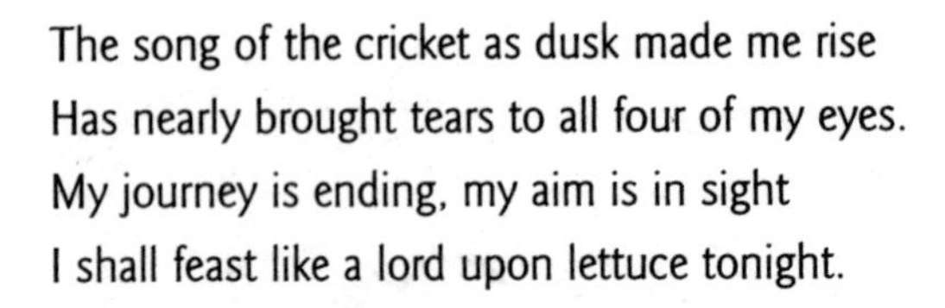

The song of the cricket as dusk made me rise
Has nearly brought tears to all four of my eyes.
My journey is ending, my aim is in sight
I shall feast like a lord upon lettuce tonight.

Penny Culliford

Snail

Snail goes down the garden
Leaving a silver track;
Snail goes down the garden
And slowly snail comes back.
No wonder snail can't hurry,
He hasn't got the knack,
And wouldn't you move slowly,
With a house upon your back?

Jack Ousbey

Message in a Space Bottle

Such strange people!
Skin of many colours,
Tiny eyes,
Fur sprouting from their heads!
A useful planet though.
Just the right size,
Wind and rain,
Seas, forests,
Green leaves though, not red,
Which takes some getting used to!

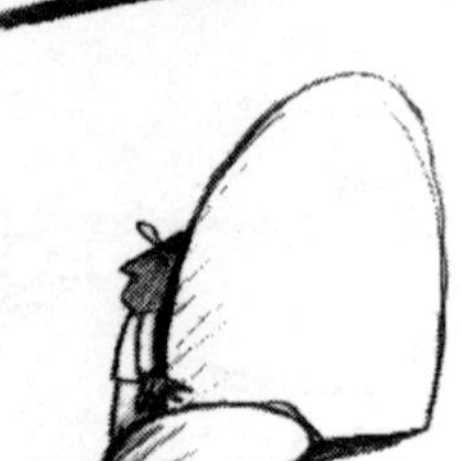

I do not know
If I shall ever
Get home.
I knew
Our ship would never fly again,
The sky
Was our prison.
If you hear me,
Please come.
Third planet from the sun.
Three dead.
Just one alive.

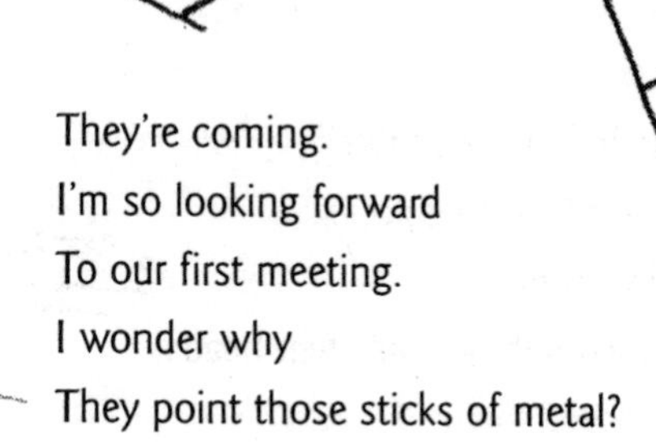

They're coming.
I'm so looking forward
To our first meeting.
I wonder why
They point those sticks of metal?

It must be a local form
Of greeting.

David Orme

Visting Jupiter

There must be some celestial M25
all the way to Jupiter,
how else can you explain
why it takes six years to get there?
Six years without a service station on the way.
Six years of stopping and starting
and travelling through roadworks,
single carriageway all the way to Venus.
And what would it be like for any spaceman
travelling there?
'Just slipping out to visit Jupiter,
see you soon, don't wait up...'
Not much scope for holidays either,
no possibilities of day trips or weekend breaks.
Six years!
What are you doing for the next six years?
Think of all the books you could read,
the games you could play – not I-spy though,
'I-spy with my little eye something beginning
with S... Yes, SPACE,
lots of it,
how did you guess?'

Brian Moses

Adventurer

When I want adventure,
there is a place I go to.
I sit quietly, close my eyes
and I am away
among dragons, flying cats,
walking, talking fish
and an old woman in a funny hat
who grants my every wish.

John Lyons

On a Camel to the Moon
(or Anything you want son)

Some people like to fly high
In a small hot air balloon,
And some will get a thrill
From a train ride to Rangoon,
It's fun, I hear, to scuba dive
Out in the Blue Lagoon,
But I'd like to ride a camel
All the way up to the moon.

I won't need the rocket fuel
So I'll save on the expense,
Inside a spaceship I have heard
The heat is quite intense.
I get bad travel sickness
In a bus, a tram or train,
But if I could ride a camel
You would not hear me complain.

Oh I'd get the greatest pleasure
Snuggled in the camel's humps,
And he doesn't ask for too much,
Just some grain and sugar lumps.
He will skim through rocky craters,
Sail through desert and sand dune,
And is just the friend you want
On a long trip to the moon.

No, Dad, please not a new pet,
No baby chimp or young baboon,
I don't want to visit Egypt
Where you spent your honeymoon,
I want a birthday present
I will not forget too soon,
So can I have a day-trip
On a camel to the moon?

Valerie Bloom

Tray

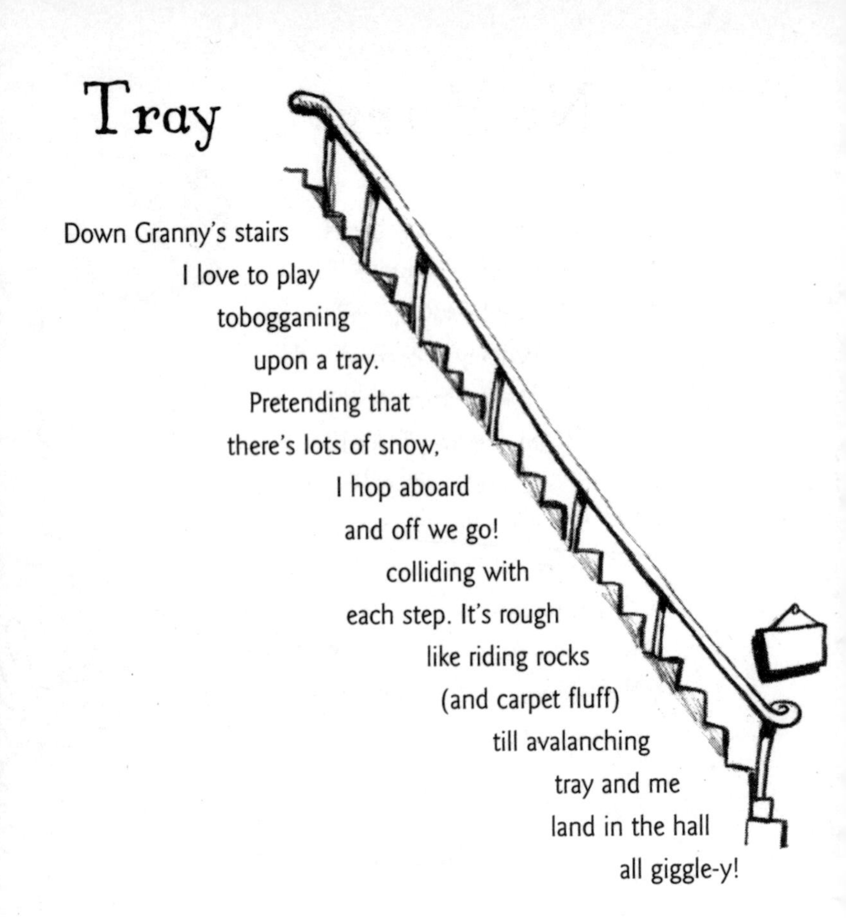

Down Granny's stairs
I love to play
tobogganing
upon a tray.
Pretending that
there's lots of snow,
I hop aboard
and off we go!
colliding with
each step. It's rough
like riding rocks
(and carpet fluff)
till avalanching
tray and me
land in the hall
all giggle-y!

Gina Douthwaite

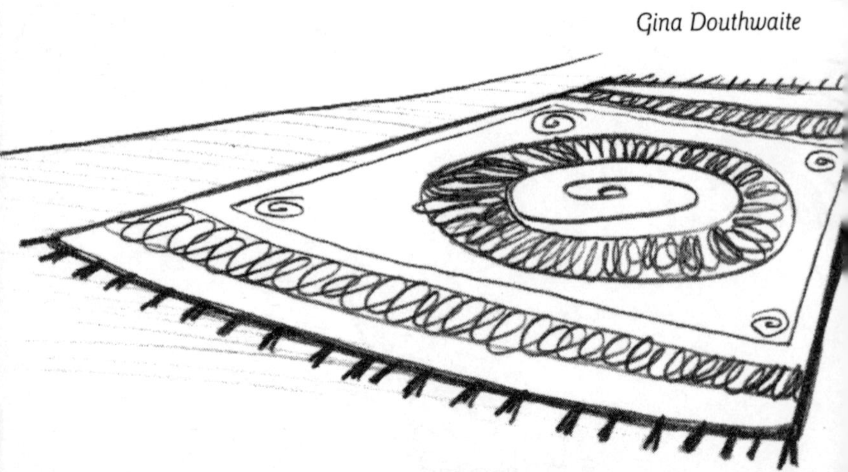

No Hurry

On the motorway banks
As we sped past,
Airily waving,
Whitely massed:
Moon daisies,
Calm and lovely-faced,
Silently asking,
'Why such haste?'

Eric Finney

A Surprise for Gerald the Sloth

It was in the bathroom
That Gerald the Sloth
Saw himself in the mirror
For the first time.
He was astounded.
The youthful glint in his eyes,
The glistening sheen of his fur,
The gentle curve of his powerful claws.

Gerald the Sloth was moved.
Moved to write poetry.
Poetry that would celebrate
His great beauty.

He wasted no time.
Out the bathroom,
Down the stairs,
Through the kitchen,
On his bike,
Down the road,
W H Smiths,
Stationery Department,
One pencil,
Note book,
Paid cash.
Then
On his bike,
Up the road,
Through the kitchen,
Up the stairs,
Into the bathroom.

Gerald the Sloth
Saw himself in the mirror
For the second time.
He was even more astounded.
Eyes: dull and blood-shot.
Fur: grey and thinning.
Claws: twisted and feeble.

Twenty-five years is a long time.

John Coldwell

Where Do I Go?

Where do I go
When I go to sleep?
When the moon shines bright,
And the shadows creep?

When pictures come,
And people talk;
and I fly like a bird,
or go for a walk;

When I take a ride,
On a dinosaur's tail;
Or swim the sea,
On the back of a whale.

You stay in your bed,
As safe as a sock;
And snooze all night,
To the tick of the clock.

John Cunliffe

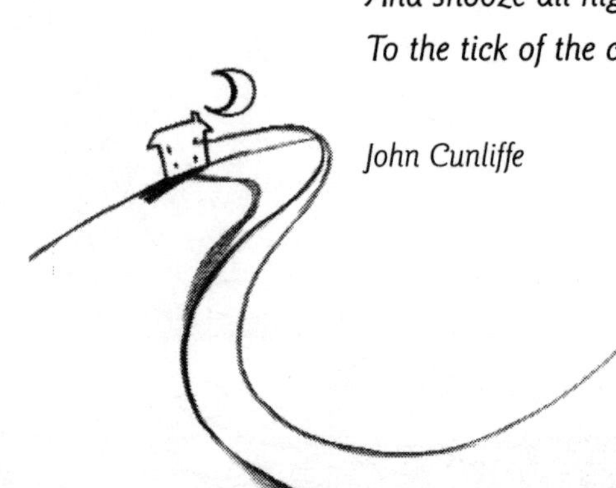

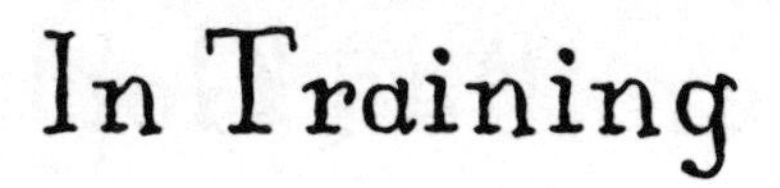

In Training

The train is at Born-Ville station.
The whistle wails and we're off to Nappily-Ever-After Land.
It's a Poo-poo train, making its way to Crawley.
All change for Childhood-on-the-Daughter.
Now we are nearly at Little Tantrum.
But things are not going our way.
The train speeds on to Big Tantrum.
The brakes screech and scream to an unscheduled stop.
There is an argument on the line,
And we are so close to the town of Kiss-And-Make-Up,
Suddenly diverted to Sulkington-On-See-Me-Later.
We might have to bypass Middle Pudding and
Head straight to Bed-Stone.
At last we have arrived at TV station.
Passengers are advised to watch out for rubbish.
Thank you for travelling on our one-to-five express!

Andrew Fusek Peters

The Owl and the Elephant
(a parody)

The Owl and the Elephant went to sea
  In a battered and leaky boat.
On account of their size, this was not very wise,
  For the boat was barely afloat.
The owl looked up as it started to rain,
  No moon nor a single star,
'O Elephant Friend, this looks like the end,
  And in terrible trouble we are,
      We are,
      We are,
  Oh in terrible trouble we are!'

The Elephant cried, and didn't feel brave,
While the wind made an awful sound.
'O what shall we do, we desperate two,
With these gigantic waves all around?'
The Owl thought awhile of the plight they were in
And only had one thing to say:
'It appears, so to speak, your future looks bleak,
Now it's time I was up and away,
Away!
Away!
Now it's time I was up and away!'

Brian D'Arcy

The Sitting Room Sailors

The Captain stood in his cardboard boat,
He raised his T-shirt sail,
'Let's roam across the Carpet Seas
To track the Treasure Trail.'

His cuddly crew drew back their oars,
His teddy manned the mast,
And though the rugs were strewn with rocks
They spotted land at last.

They reached the shores of Bathroom Bay
Where waves splashed hot and cold,
They plundered Kitchen Harbour
But they found no Spanish gold.

They crept through Backyard Jungle
Where the weeds stood thick and high,
They spied a Secret Sandpit
As the sun sank in the sky.

And there they caught the glimmer
Of a pirate's hidden hoard,
Silver coins of chocolate
To carry back on board.

They travelled home in triumph
Across the Sleepy Sea,
Then landed, safe and starry-eyed,
And just in time for tea.

Clare Bevan

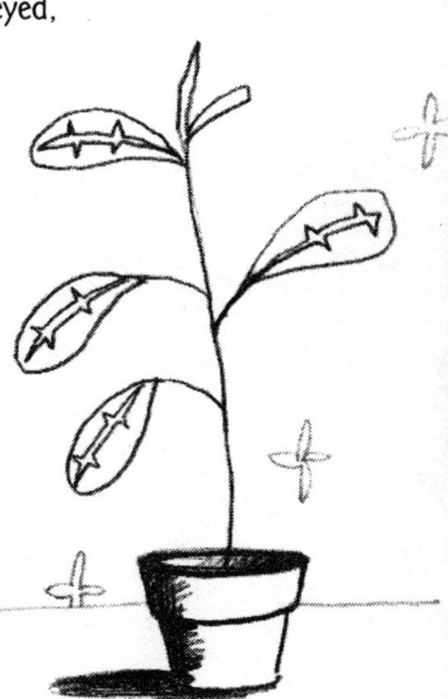

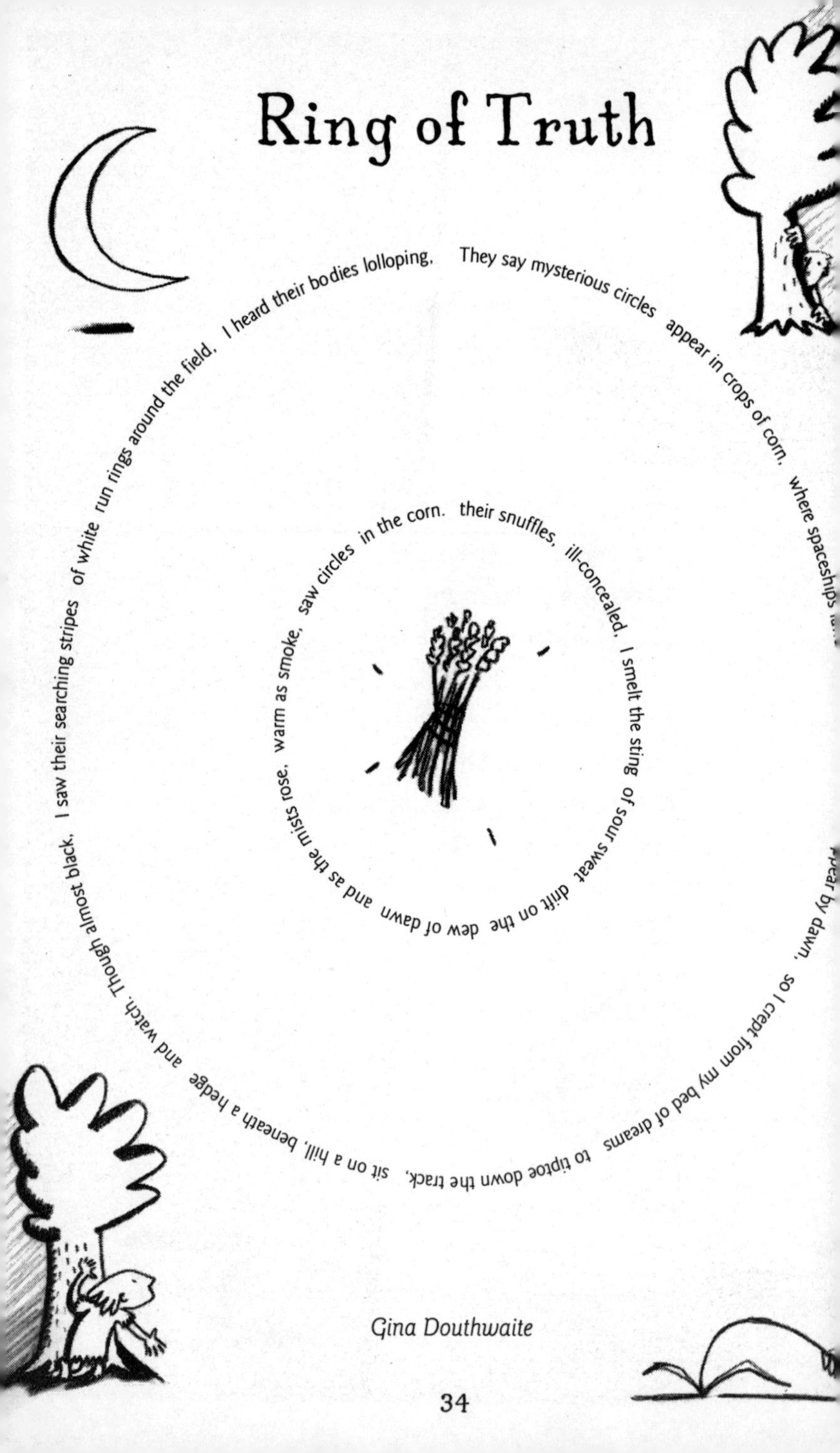

Ring of Truth

They say mysterious circles appear in crops of corn, where spaceships land appear by dawn, so I crept from my bed of dreams to tiptoe down the track, sit on a hill, beneath a hedge and watch. Though almost black, I saw their searching stripes of white run rings around the field, I heard their bodies lolloping, their snuffles, ill-concealed, I smelt the sting of sour sweat drift on the dew of dawn and as the mists rose, warm as smoke, saw circles in the corn.

Gina Douthwaite

t Is... the Beast th No Name?

(a riddle)

/aster than a galaxy
  the Beast with No Name
lithers along the spaceways,
ucking into its dark stomach
lead comets, meteorites,
ind abandoned space probes.

Vith a single nudge
  the Beast with No Name
ets the planets spinning.
ts face has never been seen.
he Beast is the colour of darkness
nd its journey across the universe is endless.

At dusk you can watch
  the Beast with No Name
olot out the sun as it passes by.
hose are not stars you see
out a billion burning spots
which itch wickedly on its thick skin.

Ves Magee

Answer: the night

The Sweep

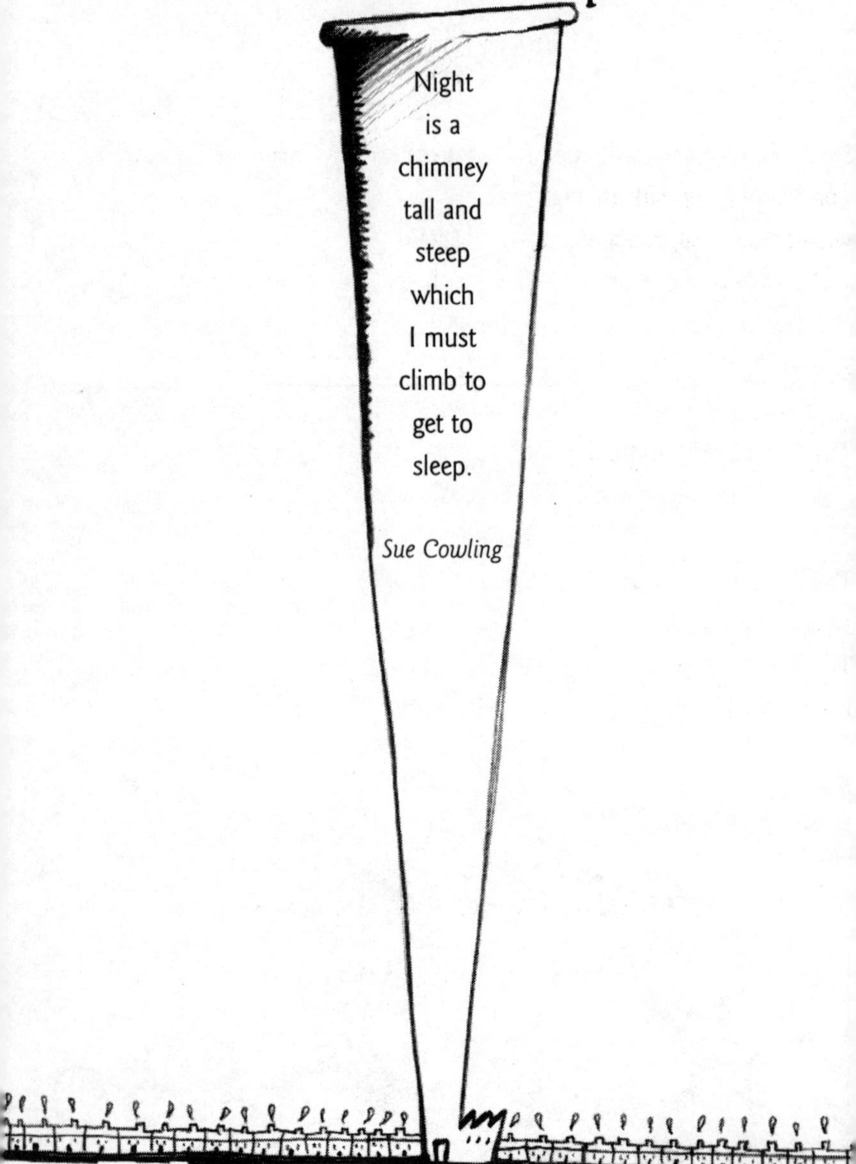

Night
is a
chimney
tall and
steep
which
I must
climb to
get to
sleep.

Sue Cowling

Ower the Sky Tae See

Over the Sky to See

Sherp starlight spikes through thinnest cloud	*sharp*
on a mountain dark an' high	
whaur deep-coat sheep bleat lang and loud	*where, long*
when a hauf moon sclims in a Scottish sky.	*half, climbs*
A selkie bobs on a glassy loch,	*seal*
the seaburds wheel an' fly.	*seabirds*
The fisher boats ignore the clock	
when a hauf moon skelps in a Scottish sky.	*half, scampers along*
The burnies gush frae glen an' brae	*streams, from, hill*
tae join the torrent's cry.	
The heather's colour is darker still	
when a hauf moon skirls in a Scottish sky.	*half, shrieks*

John Rice

Cross Country

Run in mud.
Run in rain.
Run around
the course again.

Tangled brambles.
Tripping root.
Clinging ivy.
Oaktree shoot.

Sodden field.
Dripping tree.
Cross country run
in February.

Stamina
is what I lack.
Shirt is sticking
to my back.

How much longer
till I'm there?
Hot hot shower.
Dry my hair.

I'll take my time.
Not get upset.
Pretend that I'm
not wet, wet, wet.

Ann Bonner

The Terrible Path

While playing at the woodland's edge
I saw a child one day,
She was standing near a foaming brook
And a sign half-rotted away.

There was something strange about her clothes;
They were from another age,
I might have seen them in a book
Upon a mildewed page.

She looked pale and frightened,
Her voice was thick with dread.
She spoke through lips rimmed with green
And this is what she said:

'I saw a signpost with no name,
I was surprised and had to stare,
It pointed to a broken gate
And a path that led nowhere.

'The path had run to seed and I
Walked as in a dream.
It entered a silent oak wood,
And crossed a silent stream.

'And in a tree a silent bird
Mouthed a silent song.
I wanted to turn back again
But something had gone wrong.

'The path would not let me go;
It had claimed me for its own,
It led me through a dark wood
Where all was overgrown.

'I followed it until the leaves
Had fallen from the trees,
I followed it until the frost
Drugged the autumn's bees.

'I followed it until the spring
Dissolved the winter snow,
And whichever way it turned
I was obliged to go.

'The years passed like shooting stars,
They melted and were gone,
But the path itself seemed endless,
It twisted and went on.

'I followed it and thought aloud,
"I'll be found, wait and see."
Yet in my heart I knew by then
The world had forgotten me.'

Frightened I turned homeward,
But stopped and had to stare.
I too saw that signpost with no name,
And the path that led nowhere.

Brian Patten

Only Five Stops

The bullying boys are on our bus,
They hit and kick, they spit and cuss.
They shout out the window, they bang on the glass
And I dread the moment they turn on us.

Everyone's scared, but we all know
it's better not to let it show.
They toss someone's schoolbag to and fro,
I cross my fingers. Five stops to go.

Grownups laugh when I tell them my fears:
'It's only five stops from school to here.'
They don't understand how taunts and jeers
can make five minutes seem like five years.

Mandy Coe

A Dog in the Margin

It seemed like an ordinary sort of poem
As Jim set out
from the top of the page
to visit his Nan.

Nan always bought him
A BIG ICE CREAM
But
The poet had written a surprise for Jim.

Part way down the page a

BIG DOG

Bolted from the margin
and tore along the line that Jim had reached.

The BIG DOG fastened its teeth around
Jim's terrified arm and
ripped his jumper.

'Help!' screamed Jim.
And there was Nan
dashing across the page
swinging her umbrella.

One whack of that umbrella
and off to the safety of the margin raced the

G DOG

Resolving to ambush only unarmed poems.

Meanwhile,
at the bottom of the page,
Jim ate
A BIG ICE CREAM
through trembling lips,
'It started out like such an ordinary poem,'
moaned Jim.
'Don't worry,' said Nan.
'I've repaired your sweater.
No-one will ever know.'

John Coldwell

Road Hazard

Are we nearly there yet?
Can I have a drink then?
I don't want orange.

Are we nearly there yet?
Shall we play I spy?
Counting red cars?
Spot the cow?
Buzz?

Are we nearly there yet?
Can I have some crisps?
– I don't like cheese and onion.
Are there any chocolate biscuits?
– I don't like apples.
Can we have the radio on?

I need the toilet. I can't wait.

It's raining.
Will it be raining when we get there?

e we nearly –
o... when you get cross your neck goes all bright red.
ur eyes go sort of funny –
nd of bulgy, like light bulbs in your head.
ıd your voice goes squeaky
'ell, sort of squeaky-growly-gruff
rry! Pardon me for breathing,
hought you'd like to know that stuff.

e –

think it won't be long now – Dad is driving faster
ough I can't know that for sure, since I've had a small disaster
d it's hard to ask a question when you're taped with sticking plaster.)

ı Dean

Flying a Camel

'When I was young,' the old man said,
'I joined the Flying Corps.
That, of course, was long ago
In the First World War.

'I flew a Sopwith Camel then
And liked it very much.'
'A camel!' said the little boy,
'You're talking double-dutch!'

'Not that kind! An aeroplane:
It had two wings in front,
A biplane not a monoplane;
Its nose was big and blunt.

'But it was marvellous to fly,
Simple as a kite;
The joystick sent it up or down,
The rudder left or right.'

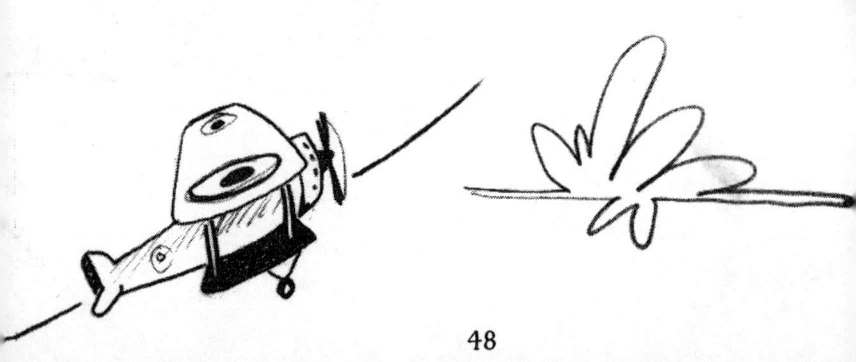

'But why a camel?' said the boy,
  'Why not a horse, or whale?'
'I'm not quite sure – maybe because
  It had a rounded tail.

'I only know it was such bliss
  When I soared high above
The clouds and dived, and soared again,
  I felt a kind of love,

'The way a horseman feels his mount
  Respond beneath his hands
And knows his horse will never fail
  To answer his demands.'

The boy said, 'Did you fight a lot
  And knock the Jerries out?'
The old man then looked sad: 'That's not
  A thing I talk about.'

Vernon Scannell

From: A Little Kite Music

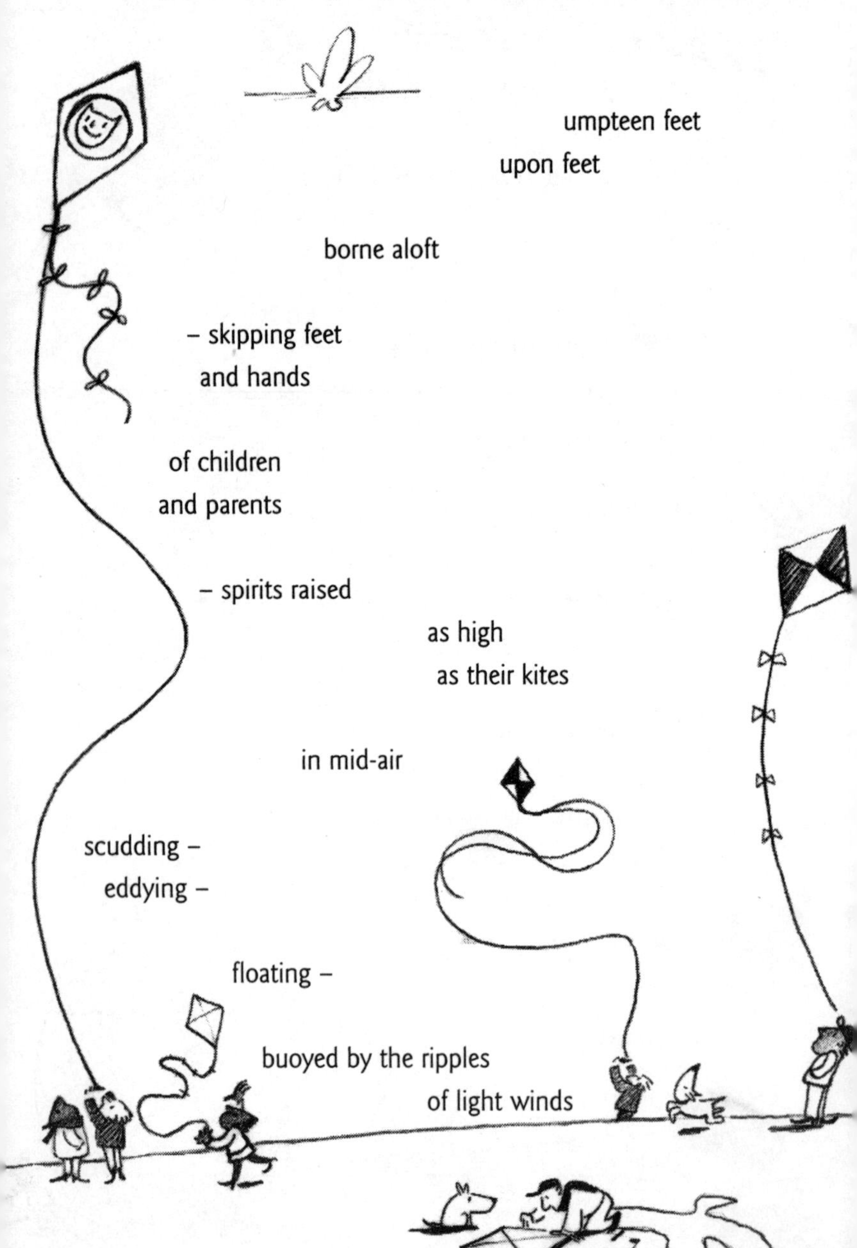

umpteen feet
upon feet

borne aloft

– skipping feet
and hands

of children
and parents

– spirits raised

as high
as their kites

in mid-air

scudding –
eddying –

floating –

buoyed by the ripples
of light winds

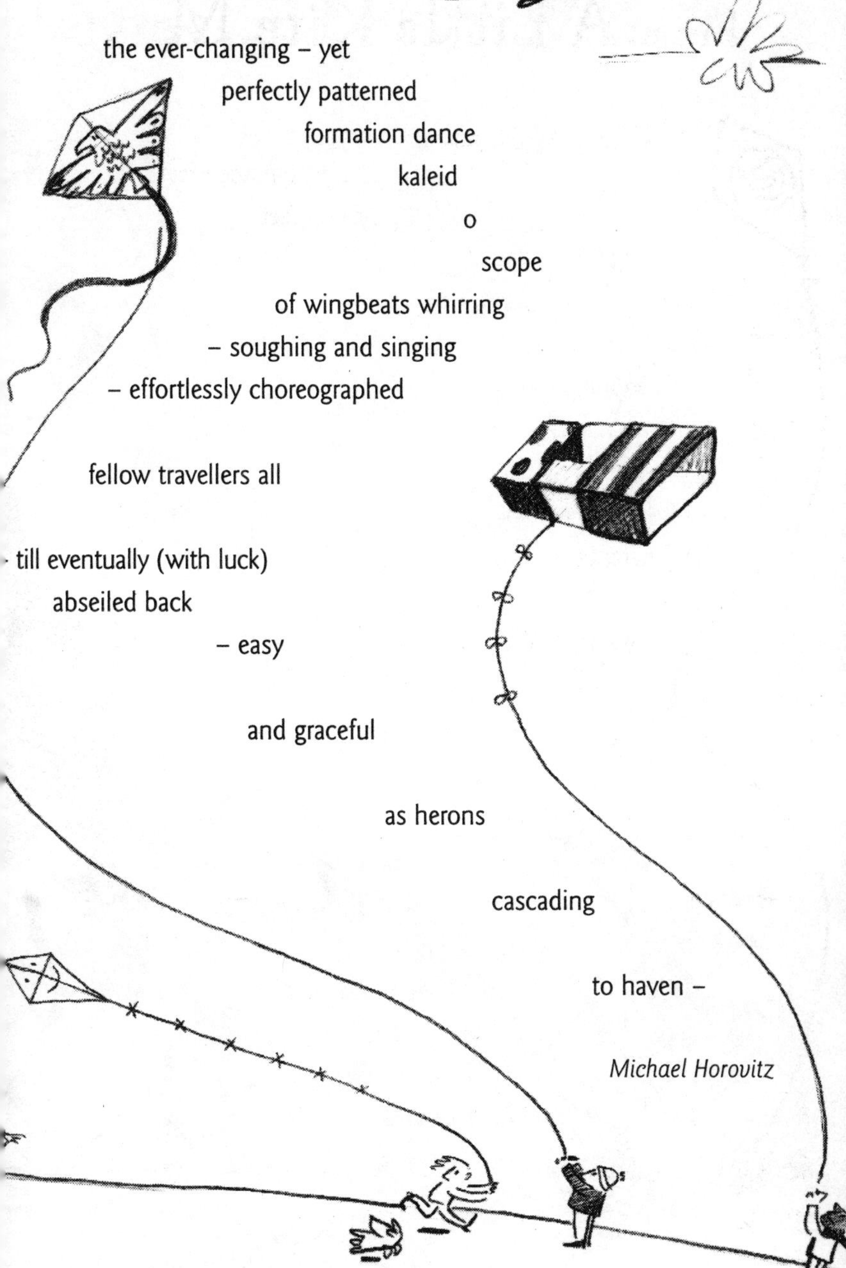

the ever-changing – yet
perfectly patterned
formation dance
kaleid
o
scope
of wingbeats whirring
– soughing and singing
– effortlessly choreographed

fellow travellers all

till eventually (with luck)
abseiled back
– easy

and graceful

as herons

cascading

to haven –

Michael Horovitz

Seven Old Ladies

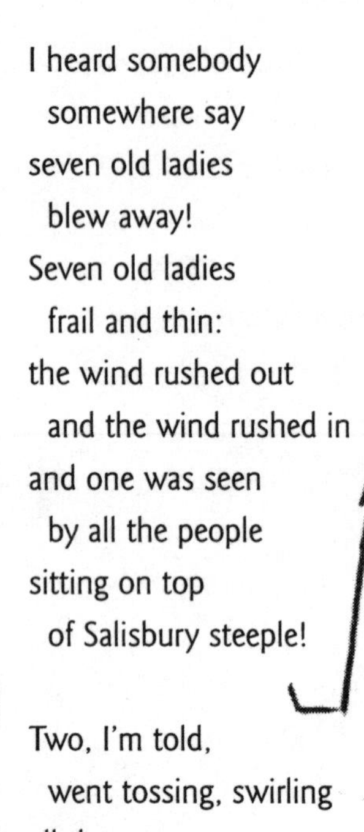

I heard somebody
  somewhere say
seven old ladies
  blew away!
Seven old ladies
  frail and thin:
the wind rushed out
  and the wind rushed in
and one was seen
  by all the people
sitting on top
  of Salisbury steeple!

Two, I'm told,
  went tossing, swirling
all the way
  from Stowe to Stirling.
Three were caught
  and counted, dancing
over the air
  from Looe to Lancing.
But the smallest
  shouted 'STOP!
Put me down
  before I drop!

'North Wind, South Wind,
  East or West –
don't you ruffle
  my Sunday vest –
don't you touch me!
  Don't you dare!
Blow the other ones
  ANYwhere
but I certainly
  will not stir...'
WHOOSH! Whatever
  became of her?

Jean Kenward

The River

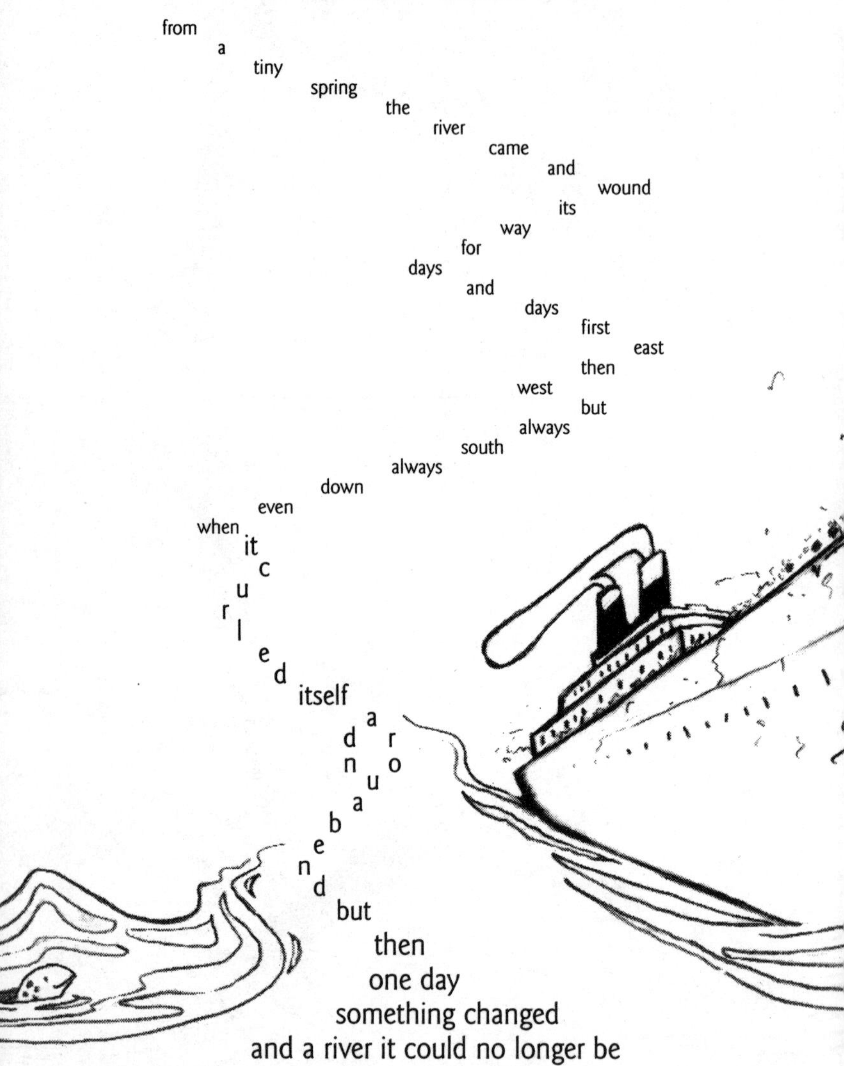

from
a
tiny
spring
the
river
came
and
wound
its
way
for
days
and
days
first
east
then
west
but
always
south
always
down
even
when
it
curled
itself
around
a
bend
but
then
one day
something changed
and a river it could no longer be
for the river grew and the river knew that now it was
THE SEA THE SEA THE SEA THE SEA THE SEA THE SEA T
SEA THE SEA THE SEA THE SEA THE SEA THE SEA THE S
THE SEA THE SEA THE SEA THE SEA THE SEA THE SEA T

E SEA THE SEA THE SEA THE SEA THE SEA THE SEA THE SEA THE
A THE SEA THE SEA THE SEA THE SEA THE SEA THE SEA THE SEA
E SEA THE SEA THE SEA THE SEA

James Carter

Classified Travel

SUMMER Vision

far away on Mars
dus waves blush as
Shakespeare the frogman floats northwards
by the secret beaches
of a great lost ocean.

A blue sun rises.
The *desert* air is thick with Raindrops.
under black skies showers sparkle.
enchanting teeth smile
by the spritzy champagne sea.

Now Come back to earth
and ride the ebbing tide
of *the* old century.

aquaplane into a future
o fdiamond days.

Penny Kent

Victoria's Statues

It amused Queen Victoria
to be Empress of India.
Although she never travelled there,
she left her statues everywhere.

Debjani Chatterjee

Carried Away

Sometimes an idea runs away with me,
And I with him.
We pack a mutual suitcase and
Go out on a limb,
We abseil down the Moon's dark side
To where delinquent gerbils hide
Chewing craters ten miles wide,
And we join in.

Sometimes my dreams run away with me:
Yes, we elope.
We climb down from my window sill
On knotted rope
And join the Assyrian merchant fleet,
Pedalo-ing triremes with our bare feet
And washing the beaches white as sleet,
Using Sunlight soap.

Sometimes my thoughts run away with me
We get carried away,
Leaving behind cunning likenesses
Of ourselves in clay;
And we save the planet from ravening crocs,
Whirling amplified birdsong in hockey socks
And posting them home in a cardboard box
At the end of the day.

Almost every day,
I get carried away.
I do, it's true:
I'm just like you.
I get carried away.

Geraldine McCaughrean

Information for Travellers

As you read this poem you are on a spacecraft
travelling at sixty-six thousand miles an hour.
It spins as it flies: since you began to read
it has already turned nine miles to the east.
Be honest, you didn't feel a thing.

You are orbiting a star, not a very big one
compared to many of the ten thousand million others
that go round on the same galactic wheel,
and are flying at a height above its surface
of some ninety-three million miles.

We hope to cruise at this distance for another
eight thousand million years. What happens then
is anybody's guess. Despite its speed and size
this craft is a spacestation, a satellite, not designed
for interstellar flight. Its passengers
rely on the comfort of a pressurized cabin
to enjoy the voyage. We must advise you that,
in the event of collision, loss of atmosphere,
or any alteration in course which may result
in overheating or extreme cold, this craft is not
equipped with parachutes or emergency exits.

On a brighter note, the spaceship contains
an enormous variety of in-flight magazines,
meals to suit every taste, and enough
games, puzzles and adventures
to last a lifetime.

We hope you enjoy your voyage.
Thank you for flying Planet Earth.

Dave Calder

Index of titles and first lines

First lines are in italics

Index of authors

Acknowledgements

Clare Bevan: 'The Sitting Room Sailors' © Clare Bevan. **Valerie Bloom**: 'In an Airplane' and 'On a Camel to the Moon' © Valerie Bloom. **Ann Bonner**: 'Cross Country' © Ann Bonner. **Dave Calder**: 'Information for Travellers' © Dave Calder. **James Carter**: 'Journey' and 'The River' © James Carter. **Debjani Chatterjee**: 'Victoria's Statues' © Debjani Chatterjee. **Gillian Clarke**: 'The Osprey' © Gillian Clarke, first published in *The Animal Wall* (Pont Books, Gomer Press). **Mandy Coe**: 'Only Five Stops' © Mandy Coe. **John Coldwell**: 'A Surprise for Gerald the Sloth' © John Coldwell, first published in *The Bee's Sneeze* (Stride, 1990); 'A Dog in the Margin' © John Coldwell, first published in *The Bee's Sneeze* (Stride, 1992). **Sue Cowling**: 'The Sweep' © Sue Cowling, first published in *A Mean Fish Smile* by Roger Stevens, Sue Cowling and Jan Dean (Macmillan, 2000). **Penny Culliford**: 'The Traveller' © Penny Culliford. **John Cunliffe**: 'Where Do I Go?' © John Cunliffe. **Brian D'Arcy**: 'The Owl and the Elephant' © Brian D'Arcy. **Jan Dean**: 'Road Hazard' © Jan Dean. **Gina Douthwaite**: 'Tray' © Gina Douthwaite; 'Ring of Truth' © Gina Douthwaite, first published in *Aliens Stole My Underpants* (Macmillan, 2001). **Eric Finney**: No Hurry' © Eric Finney, first published in *Another Fifth Poetry Book*, compiled by John Foster (Oxford University Press, 1989). **Andrew Fusek Peters**: 'In Training' © Andrew Fusek Peters. **Michael Horovitz**: the excerpt from 'A Little Kite Music' is part of section 3 of *A New Waste Land: Timeship Earth at Nillennium* © Michael Horovitz/New Departures, 2001. **Penny Kent**: 'Classified Travel, Summer Vision' © Penny Kent. **Jean Kenward**: 'Seven Old Ladies' © Jean Kenward. **John Lyons**: 'Adventurer' © John Lyons. **Wes Magee**: 'What Is... the Beast with No Name?' © Wes Magee. **Geraldine McCaughrean**: 'Carried Away' © Geraldine McCaughrean. **Michaela Morgan**: 'The Blue Yonder' © Michaela Morgan. **Brian Moses**: 'Visiting Jupiter' © Brian Moses. **Judith Nicholls**: 'Sea Dream' © Judith Nicholls 1987, from *Midnight Forest* by Judith Nicholls (Faber & Faber). Reprinted by permission of the author. **David Orme**: 'Message in a Space Bottle' © David Orme. **Jack Ousbey**: 'Snail' © Jack Ousbey. **Brian Patten**: 'The Terrible Path' © Brian Patten, first published in *Gargling with Jelly* (Puffin, 1985). **John Rice**: 'Ower the Sky Tae See' © John Rice. **Vernon Scannell**: 'Flying a Camel' © Vernon Scannell. **Nick Toczek**: 'Dragon on the Bus' © Nick Toczek.

Every effort has been made to contact copyright holders. The publishers would like to hear from any copyright holder not acknowledged.